DATE DUE

NOV 1 0 1999	

Selections
from
GERMAN
POETRY

Illustrated by Elizabeth Korolkoff

Selections
from
GERMAN
POETRY

by VLADIMIR RUS

Foreword by LOTTE LENYA

HARVEY HOUSE, INC.
Irvington-on-Hudson, New York

© 1966 by Harvey House, Inc.

Library of Congress Catalog Card Number: 66-14177
Manufactured in the United States of America

HARVEY HOUSE, INC. • Publishers
Irvington-on-Hudson • New York

Foreword

It is always a pleasure to greet a group of old friends, whether people, songs, or poems. In reading this collection of German poems my pleasure was increased by the faithfulness of the translations. They accurately render the meaning of the originals, and they also have that quality that we vaguely call the spirit of poetry—a spirit that constitutes the true value of a poem.

My delight in reading these selections was also increased by the fact that the selections cover the history of German literature from its beginnings to the most recent times. As one who has been connected in many ways with the growth of modern German letters, I have learned to understand and to appreciate the unity of the cultural life of the nation. Like the spirits in Goethe's *Faust*, the sources of good German literature and poetry ascend in an unbroken stream from its oldest monuments to the latest works of its young authors, and again lead back in a perfect ring from the most modern surrealistic poems to its origin.

To those who approach German poetry for the first time, I would like to give a word of warning as well as a word of advice: Do not expect to be easily pleased with elegant rhymes. The history of Germany is a history of one interminable war—a war fought in the field of politics, in the field of religion, in the field of art and philosophy, and frequently on all of them simultaneously, but most often on the bloody battlefields of actual war, both civil and foreign.

German poetry as a result is harsh and forbidding as often as it is beautiful and deep. Do not be offended if, at first, a German poem does not appeal to you, or if it annoys you or even outrages you. There are poems in this selection that may appeal to you at first sight, but there are also some that may disturb you and perhaps even scandalize you. If so, do not be too hasty to reject either the author or the poem. Remember that a poem can commit only one sin, and that is to leave the reader indifferent. No author of any poem in this volume will do that. All of these poems, even those that appear to be simple and innocent, are like atoms: they are full of energy, full of thought. Only your reflection as a reader will release that energy. Read all of them thoughtfully, and your effort will be rewarded by a deeper understanding of the spirit of German poetry.

LOTTE LENYA

New City, New York
May, 1966

To read a poem is to contemplate a flower. We may stop by the roadside to look at a blossom and delight in its harmony, its simplicity, and its beauty. Or we can settle down and more leisurely consider the intricate lacework of petals and pistils and filaments. Or, finally, we can marvel at the combination of elementary forces which draw the flower from its seed — a star burns in the sky to give it warmth and light, a planet has labored for millions of years to prepare the soil from which the flower grows.

And so it is with a poem. To a casual glance it shows in simplicity and harmony a picture, a scene, a thought. To a more inquisitive beholder it reveals the subtle patterns of words and rhythms, of figures and images. And always, even though invisible and unnoticed, there are the elementary forces which shape it and give it life — the mind and the temper of the poet, and the mind and the temper of the culture into which the poet was born. A flower mirrors in miniature the whole physical universe. A poem mirrors in miniature the whole world of men.

This little collection of German verse is a threefold invitation. It offers the language student an opportunity to further his study and to acquaint himself with the poetic idiom of another nation. For him, the translations preserve the impact and the meaningfulness of the original, which otherwise might be lost in struggling with unfamiliar phrases.

But it is also an invitation to poetry itself. A translator must to some degree read not only the original poem but also the mind of the poet who wrote it. A good translation is both transposition into another language and, at the same time, an interpretation. To those who understand German and perhaps know the poems, reading the original and the English version should afford the pleasure of another and deeper look at the familiar lines.

And finally, by including poems covering a period from the ancient times of German literature to the most recent years, this collection suggests the vast universe of thoughts and struggles from which these poems grew. Suggests only, because no single collection could adequately represent even one part of those struggles or interpret one part of those thoughts.

It is appropriate to say that German letters were and are born out of the struggle of opposites. A brief glance at the map of Europe can give us a partial suggestion as to why this is so. The European shores outline clearly the boundaries of all major nations: England, Spain, Italy, Russia, France, the Scandinavian lands — all can be clearly seen at a cursory glance. They are defined by the sea and by the mountains. But we have to look closer to discover Germany. It is neither a peninsula, nor an island, nor a mountain enclosure. Open toward the east, with only hills and a river in the west, Germany is truly, as it has been called, "the land of the middle," in which the influences of the East and of the West meet and clash.

Not only in this geographic and historical sense is Germany the "land of the middle." As if the landscape has lent its character to the people who inhabit it, the German thinkers and poets seem to be forever inclined to view life not as a harmonious whole, but as a meeting ground on which two extremes clash — the mind and matter, freedom and necessity, man and God. The story of German culture is the story of attempts to reconcile such extremes. The history of German thought is no less turbulent than German history.

As a consequence, German letters rarely offer restful vistas. To read a German novel, play, story, or poem, is to be questioned, challenged, and disturbed. Long before the term became fashionable, German literature was an existentialist literature. The question of the meaning of life is forever in it, and the wonder of contradictory forces which shape our being. And there is in it despair at the impossibility of reconciling these forces. We may disagree with such a view of life, but we cannot disregard it any more than we can disregard the beautiful and lurid world of Greek tragedy.

The study of foreign languages has recently been conditioned primarily by events in the field of science and technology. But we cannot afford to be experts in the world of machines and walk blindly through the world of men. This little volume leads from language to literature and thus, we hope, contributes in a modest way to the discovery of the men who use the language, of the craftsmen who wield the tool.

V.R.

Contents

*TRANSLATION BY THE EDITOR

                    *TRANSLATION BY THE EDITOR

*TRANSLATION BY THE EDITOR

The Prayer of Wessobrunn

This I have learned among men as the greatest of wonders:
That earth did not always exist, nor heavens,
That once there was neither forest, nor mountain,
Neither glittering stars, nor the sun did shine,
Nor moon was, nor the beautiful sea.

And while there was nothing but empty space,
Yet there was the one and almighty God,
Mildest of men, and many with Him
Were the godlike spirits. . . .

Anonymous; c. 800; one of the oldest monuments of German literature.

The Christian gospel had only recently been brought to Germany, and, for the monk who penned this fragment, it is still full of freshness and wonder.

Das erfuhr ich unter den Menschen als der Wunder größtes,
Daß Erde nicht war, noch Himmel oben,
Noch Baum, noch Berg war,
Noch irgendein Stern, noch Sonne schien,
Noch der Mond erglänzte, noch das herrliche Meer.

Als da nichts war von Enden und Wenden,
Da war der eine allmächtige Gott,
Der Mannen mildester, und mit Ihm viele
Göttliche Geister. . . .

ANONYMOUS

Under the Lime Tree

Under the lime tree
Down by the meadow
Sat my lad, and I, his lass.
You can find now
How we both
Broke the flowers and the grass.
From the woods and from the dale,
Tralalala,
Sang so sweet a nightingale.

I came a-walking
To the meadow;
My sweetheart was already there.
He received me —
Holy Mary!
What a happy pair we were!
You ask if he kissed me oft?
Tralalala,
Look, my lips are red and soft.

He had made
A bed for two
All of flowers smelling sweet,
If someone passes
By the meadow,
Surely he will laugh at it:
From the crushed and broken rose,
Tralalala,
He can guess my head's repose.

Unter der Linden,
An der Heide,
Wo ich mit meinem Liebsten saß,
Da mögt ihr finden
Wie wir beide
Die Blumen brachen und das Gras.
Vor dem Wald in einem Tal,
Tandaradei,
Sang so schön die Nachtigall.

Ich kam gegangen
Zu der Aue,
Mein Liebster war schon vor mir dort.
Da ward ich empfangen
Hehre Fraue!
Daß ich bin selig immerfort.
Hat er mich wohl oft geküßt?
Tandaradei,
Seht, wie rot mein Mund noch ist.

Er hatte gemacht
Uns ein Bette
Aus süßen Blumen mancherlei.
Des wird gelacht
Herzlich, ich wette,
Wenn jemand geht am Pfad vorbei.
An den Rosen er wohl mag,
Tandaradei,
Merken, wo das Haupt mir lag.

If others knew
How we fared,
God forbid, but I would cry.
How he kissed me,
What he dared,
None must know but he and I
And the little nightingale.
Tralalala,
I hope he won't tell the tale.

Walther von der Vogelweide; c. 1170-1230. The bulk of his work consists of thoughtfully patriotic poetry which has endeared him to all generations of Germans.

Despite its apparent simplicity, this song reveals the high poetical culture of the first golden age of German literature in the 12th century.

Wie wir da lagen,
Wenn's wer wüßte,
Behüte Gott, ich schämte mich.
Was er durft' wagen,
Wie er küßte,
Erfahre niemand als er und ich,
Und ein kleines Vögelein,
Tandaradei,
Das wird wohl verläßlich sein.

WALTHER VON DER VOGELWEIDE

And now the maiden and the man,
Isolde fair and bold Tristan
Have drunk the draught. Without delay
Over their hearts to hold her sway
Came Love, all world's restlessness,
Hearts' waylayer, their chief distress.
Before they understood their plight
She changed their hearing and their sight,
And their two souls, their bodies two
Into one soul, one body grew.
And naught was left, naught would remain
That used to sunder them in twain.
Bold Tristan loves, and fair Isolt
No more abhors him as of old.
Whom Love has touched, in him all trace
Of hate has vanished. And Love stays.
She cleansed their eyes and made them pure
And filled them with desire and lure.
Their joys and sorrows, strange to say,
Were but one in wondrous way.
If she was hurt, he felt the pain;
Isolt felt Tristan's wounds again. . . .

Gottfried von Straßburg, 12-13th century. Nothing is known about him except his name.

In his great epos, TRISTAN AND ISOLT, Gottfried celebrated brilliantly the earthly love of man and woman, and thus provided an interesting contrast to the highly spiritual idea of love in PARZIVAL of Wolfram von Eschenbach.

Sobald den Trank die Magd, der Mann,
Isot gekostet und Tristan,
Hatte Minne schon sich eingestellt.
Sie, die zu schaffen macht der Welt,
Die nach allen Herzen pflegt zu stellen,
In die Herzen schlich sie den Gesellen
Und ließ, von beiden ungesehn,
Schon ihre Siegesfahne wehn:
Sie zog sie ohne Widerstreit
Unter ihre Macht und Herrlichkeit.
Da wurden eins und einerlei
Die zweifalt waren erst und zwei:
Nicht mehr entzweit war jetzt ihr Sinn,
Isoldens Haß war ganz dahin.
Die Sühnerin, Frau Minne,
Hatte beider Sinne,
Von Haß so ganz gereinigt,
In Liebe sie vereinigt,
Daß eins so lauter und so klar
Dem andern wie ein Spiegel war.
Sie hatten beide nur ein Herz:
Sein Verdruß schuf ihr den größten Schmerz,
Ihr Schmerz verdroß ihn mächtig,
Sie waren beid' einträchtig. . . .

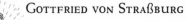

GOTTFRIED VON STRAßBURG

Psalm 90

1. A prayer of Moses man of God. Lord, Thou hast been our dwelling place in all generations.

2. Before the mountains were brought forth, or even Thou hadst formed the earth and the world, even from everlasting to everlasting, Thou art God.

3. Thou turnst man to destruction; and sayest, Return, ye children of men.

4. For a thousand years in Thy sight are but as yesterday when it is past, and as a watch in the night.

5. Thou carriest them away as with a flood; they are as a sleep: in the morning they are like grass which groweth up.

6. In the morning it flourisheth, and growth up; In the evening it is cut down, and withereth.

7. For we are consumed by Thine anger, and by Thy wrath are we troubled.

8. Thou hast set our iniquities before Thee, our secret sins in the light of Thy countenance.

9. For all our days are passed away in Thy wrath; we spend our years as a tale that is told.

1. Ein Gebet Moses, des Mannes Gottes. Herr Gott, Du bist unsre Zuflucht für und für.

2. Ehe denn die Berge wurden, und die Erde und die Welt geschaffen wurden, bist Du, Gott, von Ewigkeit zu Ewigkeit,

3. der Du die Menschen lässest sterben, und sprichst: Kommt wieder, Menschenkinder!

4. Denn tausend Jahre sind vor Dir wie der Tag, der gestern vergangen ist, und wie eine Nachtwache.

5. Du lässest sie dahinfahren wie einen Strom, und sind wie ein Schlaf; gleich wie ein Gras, das doch bald welk wird,

6. das da frühe blühet und bald welk wird, und des Abends abgehauen wird und verdorret.

7. Das machet Dein Zorn, da wir so vergehen, und Dein Grimm, dar wir so plötzlich dahin müssen.

8. Denn unsre Missetaten stellest Du vor Dich, unsre unerkannte Sünde ins Licht vor Deinem Angesichte.

9. Darum fahren alle unsre Tage dahin durch Deinen Zorn; wir bringen unsre Jahre zu wie ein Geschwätz.

10. The days of our years are threescore years and ten; and if by reason of strength they be fourscore years, yet is their strength labour and sorrow; for it is soon cut off, and we fly away.

From the King James Version of
The Book of Psalms

Martin Luther, 1483-1546. No religious controversy could diminish the greatness of his literary labors.

Luther's translation of the Holy Writ is an ever-flowing source of all the power and poetry of the German language.

10. Unser Leben währet siebenzig Jahre, und wenn's hoch kommt, so sind's achtzig Jahre, und wenn's köstlich gewesen ist, so ist's Mühe und Arbeit gewesen: denn es fahret schnell dahin, als flögen wir davon.

MARTIN LUTHER

Annie of Tharaw, my true love of old,
She is my life, and my good, and my gold.
Annie of Tharaw, her heart once again
To me has surrendered in joy and in pain.
Annie of Tharaw, my riches, my good,
Thou, O my soul, my flesh, and my blood!

Then come the wild weather, come sleet or come snow,
We will stand by each other, however it blow.
Oppression, and sickness, and sorrow, and pain,
Shall be to our true love as links to the chain.
Annie of Tharaw, my light and my sun,
The threads of our two lives are woven in one.

Translated by HENRY W. LONGFELLOW

Simon Dach; 1605-59. The depth of his individual sentiment, uncommon in his time, anticipated the modern German poetry since Goethe.

The earnest simplicity of feeling and a winsome melody made of this wedding lay one of the most widely beloved songs of the German nation.

Ännchen von Tharau ist, die mir gefällt,
Sie ist mein Leben, mein Gut und mein Geld.
Ännchen von Tharau hat wieder ihr Herz
Auf mich gerichtet in Lieb' und in Schmerz;
Ännchen von Tharau, mein Reichtum, mein Gut,
Du meine Seele, mein Fleisch und mein Blut.

Käm' alles Wetter gleich auf uns zu schlahn,
Wir sind gesinnt beieinander zu stahn!
Krankheit, Verfolgung, Betrübnis und Pein
Soll uns'rer Liebe Verknotigung sein.
Ännchen von Tharau, mein Licht und mein' Sonn',
Mein Leben schließ' ich um deines herum.

SIMON DACH

The Cherubinic Pilgrim (Selections)

You Cannot Grasp God
God is a Naught, unmoved by Nows and Heres,
The more you seek him out, the farther He appears.

Man Is Eternity
I am Eternity when I shake off Time
And climb into God's heart, into mine let Him climb.

I Am Like God and God Is Like Me
I am as high as God, He is as I so low,
He cannot rise above, I cannot fall below.

Angelus Silesius (pseudonym of Johannes Scheffler); 1624-77. He examined boldly with other poets of the German baroque the relation of man to God.

The ancient idea of the mystical identity of God and man is again emerging in our century as one of the focal points of theological thought.

Gott ergreift man nicht

Gott ist ein lauter Nichts, Ihn rührt kein Nun noch Hier.
Je mehr du nach Ihm greifst, je mehr entwird Er dir.

Der Mensch ist Ewigkeit

Ich selbst bin Ewigkeit, wann ich die Zeit verlasse
Und mich in Gott und Gott in mich zusammenfasse.

Ich bin wie Gott und Gott wie ich

Ich bin so groß als Gott, Er ist als ich so klein:
Er kann nicht über mich, ich unter Ihm nicht sein.

ANGELUS SILESIUS

My Silent Pipe!

My silent pipe! My flute of peace!
When yearningly with my firm teeth
Your stem I grip, please do not slip!
With every whiff and every puff
I chase a care, a fear I doff.
And as your smoke with curling swells
Shies off the gnats, it also quells
Each bee which in my bonnet dwells.
My quiet flute! My silent pipe!
When yearningly your stem I gripe
With my firm teeth, don't break! Just breathe!

Daniel Stoppe, 1697-1747. The praise of wordly pleasures belonged in his time to one of the traditions engendered by the tragic events of the Thirty Years' War.

The experience of smoking was still relatively novel when Stoppe wrote his Tobacco Cantata *from which this aria is taken.*

Stille Flöte! Stumme Pfeife!
Wenn ich lechzend nach dir greife,
So halt doch redlich aus und brich mir nicht entzwei!
Deiner Züge leises Baffen
Kann mir Trost und Lindrung schaffen.
Wie der Rauch die Bienen scheucht,
Ebenso verfliegt und weicht
Von deiner Melodie der Grillen Phantasei.
Stille Flöte! Stumme Pfeife!
Wenn ich lechzend nach dir greife,
So halt doch redlich aus und brich mir nicht entzwei!

DANIEL STOPPE

I found her in the shade of spring,
I bound her with a wreath of roses;
She felt it not, and slumbered on.

I looked at her, and in my glance
My life became with hers but one,
I felt it, but I knew it not.

I whispered softly in her ears,
And rustled with the wreath of roses,
Then from her slumber she awoke.

She looked at me, and in her glance
Her life became with mine but one,
And all around was paradise.

Friedrich Gottlieb Klopstock (1724-1803) prepared the ground for the second golden age of German literature by overcoming the rationalism of the 18th century in his monumental epos, THE MESSIAH.

A beauty sleeping amidst roses was a favorite love symbol of the rococo poets.

Im Frühlingsschatten fand ich sie,
Da band ich sie mit Rosenbändern;
Sie fühlt' es nicht und schlummerte.

Ich sah sie an: mein Leben hing
Mit diesem Blick an ihrem Leben:
Ich fühlt' es wohl, und wußt' es nicht.

Doch lispelt' ich ihr sprachlos zu
Und rauschte mit den Rosenbändern:
Da wachte sie vom Schlummer auf.

Sie sah mich an; ihr Leben hing
Mit diesem Blick an meinem Leben
Und um uns ward's Elysium.

FRIEDRICH GOTTLIEB KLOPSTOCK

The Mother by the Cradle

Sleep, darling boy, so sweet and mild,
Your father's joy, his own true child.
You look like him, though he declares
Your nose is not the one he wears.

He just was here, and thoughtfully
He murmured, "I suppose
The chin and eyes he got from me,
But that is not my nose."

I think so too, it's far too small,
It almost is no nose at all,
But, if the nose is counterfeit,
Just where could you have gotten it?

Sleep, child, what father says of you
He only speaks in jest.
Though you don't have his nose, it's true,
His heart is in your breast.

Translated by JOHN W. THOMAS

Matthias Claudius (1740-1815) filled his poems with the trust-ing faith, unspoiled joys, and homely truths of simple people.

Claudius' family scenes reflect his belief in the natural goodness of man, a thought which became a moving force in the political philosophies of the 19th century.

Schlaf, süßer Knabe, süß und mild!
Du deines Vaters Ebenbild!
Das bist du; zwar dein Vater spricht,
Du habest seine Nase nicht.

Nur eben jetzo war er hier
Und sah dir ins Gesicht
Und sprach: "Viel hat er zwar von mir,
Doch meine Nase nicht."

Mich dünkt es selbst, sie ist zu klein,
Doch muß es seine Nase sein;
Denn wenn's nicht seine Nase wär',
Wo hättst du denn die Nase her?

Schlaf, Knabe; was dein Vater spricht,
Spricht er wohl nur im Scherz.
Hab' immer seine Nase nicht,
Und habe nur sein Herz!

MATTHIAS CLAUDIUS

Song of Lynceus the Watchman

Born to use my eyes,
Paid to use my sight,
Sworn to guard the city,
All is my delight.
I behold the distant,
I look on the near,
The moon and the heavens,
The wood and the deer.
Fair must be my God,
For all His world is fair,
Good am I myself,
For all's good in His care.
True, my happy eyes:
Whate'er you have seen
In the gloom or sunshine
Beautiful has been.

Johann Wolfgang von Goethe (1749-1832) explored all the essential ideas of mankind and thus became an undisputed prince of German letters.

This song, taken from the second part of the tragedy FAUST, expresses the serene wisdom of the aging Goethe.

Zum Sehen geboren,
Zum Schauen bestellt,
Dem Turme geschworen
Gefällt mir die Welt.
Ich blick' in die Ferne,
Ich seh' in der Näh'
Den Mond und die Sterne,
Den Wald und das Reh.
So seh' ich in allen
Die ewige Zier,
Und wie mir's gefallen,
Gefall' ich auch mir.
Ihr glücklichen Augen,
Was je ihr gesehn,
Es sei wie es wolle,
Es war doch so schön!

JOHANN WOLFGANG VON GOETHE

Columbus

Sail on, oh captain! Though the mockers grin
And though the helm slip from a heedless hand,
Forever westward! There is a land
Which shall receive you. You have seen
Its shore before your eyes. Trust your skills.
Though oceans may be empty on their verge —
You willed a land. It shall rise from the surge.
For nature always yields what human spirit wills.

Friedrich von Schiller (1759-1805), a poet-philosopher who sought to develop the Greek ideal of the harmonious man on the basis of Kant's philosophy.

For Schiller, ideal and reality are one: the ocean yields a new continent because Columbus wills it, but Columbus can will only what exists.

Steure, mutiger Segler! Es mag der Witz dich verhöhnen,
Und der Schiffer am Steu'r senken die lässige Hand.
Immer, immer nach West! Dort muß die Küste sich zeigen,
Liegt sie doch deutlich und liegt schimmernd vor deinem Verstand.
Traue dem leitenden Gott und folge dem schweigenden Weltmeer!
Wär' sie noch nicht, sie stieg' jetzt aus den Fluten empor.
Mit dem Genius steht die Natur im ewigen Bunde;
Was der eine verspricht, leistet die andre gewiß.

FRIEDRICH VON SCHILLER

Voice of the People

Thou art the voice of God. In my sacred youth
I felt it deeply, yes, and I say it still.
But unregardful of my wisdom
Murmur the waters their own; yet ever

I love to hear them; often they move my heart
And raise the yearning spirit, the mighty ones;
And though not my way, yet securely
Downward they wander into the ocean.

Translated by JOHN ROTHENSTEINER

Friedrich Hölderlin (1770-1843) attempted to reconcile the contradiction of religious experience and rational limits in the human being.

This short poem illustrates admirably Hölderlin's central theme — the ultimate unity of the human and the divine element.

Du seiest Gottes Stimme, so ahndet' ich
   In heiliger Jugend; ja, und ich sag' es noch.—
      Um meine Weisheit unbekümmert
         Rauschen die Wasser doch auch, und dennoch

Hör' ich sie gern, und öfters bewegen sie
   Und stärken mir das Herz, die gewaltigen;
      Und meine Bahn nicht, aber richtig
         Wandeln ins Meer sie die Bahn hinunter.

FRIEDRICH HÖLDERLIN

Her Heart

Her heart was free of sorrow,
With every joy was blessed
When she her dearest infant
Held warmly to her breast.

She kissed his cheeks, his dimples,
She kissed her handsome boy,
His sturdy little figure
Filled her with love and joy.

Novalis (pseudonym of Friedrich Leopold von Hardenberg),
1772-1801. In his visionary poems he glorified night as the mother
of light and life.

The overflow of feeling in the work of the great romanticists is
deceptive. Their goal was universality, not one-sidedness. Novalis
was a lawyer by profession and a political thinker.

Ihr Herz war voller Freuden,
Von Freuden sie nur wußt',
Sie wußt' von keinem Leiden,
Drückts Kindelein an ihr' Brust.

Sie küßt' ihm seine Wangen,
Sie küßt' es mannigfalt,
Mit Liebe war sie umfangen
Durch Kindleins schöne Gestalt.

NOVALIS

Lullaby

Softly, softly, softly croon,
Sing a whispered lullaby,
Learn the music from the moon
Moving still across the sky.

Sing a melody as tender
As the brook along the stones,
As the bees around the linden —
Humming, murmured, whispered tones.

Translated by JOHN W. THOMAS

Clemens Brentano, 1778-1842. His life and his work were a flight from the corruption of civilization into the simplicity of nature.

Meaning is secondary to the sound of words in this song, which anticipates the musicalization of German poetry in the 19th century.

Singet leise, leise, leise,
Singt ein flüsternd Wiegenlied,
Von dem Monde lernt die Weise,
Der so still am Himmel zieht.

Singt ein Lied so süß gelinde,
Wie die Quellen auf den Kieseln,
Wie die Bienen um die Linde
Summen, murmeln, flüstern, rieseln.

CLEMENS BRENTANO

The Hostess' Daughter

Three merry students went 'cross the Rhine
And stopped in a tavern to dine and to wine.

"Mine hostess, have you good beer and wine?
And where is your daughter, our sweetheart fine?"

"Cool is my beer and fresh is my wine,
And in her casket that daughter of mine."

And as to the chamber they made their way,
In a black coffin the maiden lay.

The first, the veil from her face he took
And gazed at her with a mournful look:

"Fair maiden, fair maiden, why passed you away?
I'd love you, I'd love you from this day."

The second, he lightly put back the shroud
And turned away and wept aloud:

"Ah, that you lie so still on your bier,
I loved you, I loved you so many a year."

The last one again took off that veil
And kissed her on her lips so pale:

"I love you today as I loved of yore,
And so will I love you forevermore."

Ludwig Uhland (1787-1862) successfully re-created folk art in his ballads and songs.

Loyalty is treasured by Germans above all other virtues.

Es zogen drei Bursche wohl über den Rhein,
Bei einer Frau Wirtin da kehrten sie ein.

"Frau Wirtin, hat sie gut Bier und Wein?
Wo hat sie ihr schönes Töchterlein?"

"Mein Bier und Wein ist frisch und klar.
Mein Töchterlein liegt auf der Totenbahr'."

Und als sie traten zur Kammer hinein,
Da lag sie in einem schwarzen Schrein.

Der erste, der schlug den Schleier zurück
Und schaute sie an mit traurigem Blick:

"Ach, lebtest du noch, du schöne Maid!
Ich würde dich lieben von dieser Zeit."

Der zweite deckte den Schleier zu
Und kehrte sich ab und weinte dazu:

"Ach, daß du liegst auf der Totenbahr'!
Ich hab' dich geliebet so manches Jahr."

Der dritte hub ihn wieder sogleich
Und küßte sie an den Mund so bleich:

"Dich lieb' ich immer, dich lieb' ich noch heut
Und werde dich lieben in Ewigkeit."

LUDWIG UHLAND

Moonlit Night

It was as if the heavens
Had kissed the earth to sleep,
That she amid her blossoms
The glorious dream might keep.

The wind blew o'er the cornfield
And shook each golden ear.
The forests murmured softly,
The night was starry clear.

My longing soul unfolded
Her wings to rise and roam
O'er field and wood and mountain
As if she sought her home.

Translated by JOHN ROTHENSTEINER

Joseph von Eichendorff, 1788-1857. His texts inspired Franz Schubert to write some of his most beautiful songs.

The moonlit night is for Eichendorff, as for so many romanticists, a symbol of the nostalgia for man's true home in heaven.

Es war, als hätt' der Himmel
Die Erde still geküßt,
Daß sie im Blütenschimmer
Von ihm nun träumen müßt'.

Die Luft ging durch die Felder,
Die Ähren wogten sacht,
Es rauschten leis die Wälder,
So sternklar war die Nacht.

Und meine Seele spannte
Weit ihre Flügel aus,
Flog durch die stillen Lande,
Als flöge sie nach Haus.

JOSEPH VON EICHENDORFF

The Song of the Swallow

Out of Life's young May, out of Life's young May
Rings a birdsong's haunting sigh;
Oh, how far away, oh, how far away
What then was mine.

What the swallow sang, what the swallow sang,
She that fall and springtide brings,
Sounds it still along, sounds it still along
Each fall and spring?

"When I said farewell, when I said farewell,
Full stood wardrobe, chest, and stall;
Now I come to tell, now I come to tell
'Tis vanished all."

O sweet childhood's lore, O sweet childhood's lore,
Rich as Solomon, the wisest king,
I can tell no more, I can tell no more
What wildbirds sing.

Yet, dear childhood's home, yet, dear childhood's home,
Would that I could find thy door;
Let the wand'rer come, let the wand'rer come
To thee once more.

Aus der Jugendzeit, aus der Jugendzeit
Klingt ein Lied mir immerdar;
O wie liegt so weit, o wie liegt so weit
Was mein einst war.

Was die Schwalbe sang, was die Schwalbe sang,
Die den Herbst und Frühling bringt;
Ob das Dorf entlang, ob das Dorf entlang
Das jetzt noch klingt?

"Als ich Abschied nahm, als ich Abschied nahm,
Waren Kisten und Kasten schwer;
Als ich wieder kam, als ich wieder kam,
War alles leer."

O du Kindermund, o du Kindermund,
Unbewußter Weisheit froh,
Vogelsprachekund, vogelsprachekund
Wie Salomo!

O du Heimatflur, o du Heimatflur,
Laß zu deinem heil'gen Raum
Mich noch einmal nur, mich noch einmal nur
Entfliehn im Traum!

When I said farewell, when I said farewell,
All the world seemed rich and rare,
Now I come to tell, now I come to tell,
False was its glare.

Translated by JOHN ROTHENSTEINER

Friedrich Rückert (1788-1866) enriched German letters with translations and imitations of Oriental literatures.

The third verse of this haunting song was originally a folk ditty imitating the voice of the swallow.

Als ich Abschied nahm, als ich Abschied nahm,
War die Welt mir voll so sehr;
Als ich wieder kam, als ich wieder kam,
War alles leer.

FRIEDRICH RÜCKERT

Farewell to Life

My wound is burning, my lips throb and quake;
I feel my heart grow wan, and halt, and break.
Life drains from me like waters from a hill.
Lord, I am yours. Do with me as you will.

And golden dreams come swarming through my head
To weep and mourn around my dying bed.
Be still, my heart. What you have kept in trust
Shall live with me beyond the grave and dust.

My life was brief, my youth was eager flames
Which rashly sought you, God, under the guise
Of Freedom, Love, and many other names.

These all stand by me like an angel bright
And, as my senses fail me one by one,
He wafts me with his song on to the sunlit height.

Theodor Körner (1791-1813), a dashing soldier and a poet of great promise, met his untimely end in the war of liberation against Napoleon.

This poem was composed in June, 1813, when Körner, gravely wounded, lay helpless for several hours on a battlefield.

Die Wunde brennt; die bleichen Lippen beben. —
Ich fühl's an meines Herzens matterm Schlage,
Hier steh ich an den Marken meiner Tage —
Gott, wie du willst! dir hab' ich mich ergeben. —

Viel goldne Bilder sah ich um mich schweben;
Das schöne Traumbild wird zur Totenklage. —
Mut! Mut! — Was ich so treu im Herzen trage,
Das muß ja doch dort ewig mit mir leben! —

Und was ich hier als Heiligtum erkannte,
Wofür ich rasch und jugendlich entbrannte,
Ob ich's nun Freiheit, ob ich's Liebe nannte:

Als lichten Seraph seh' ich's vor mir stehen; —
Und wie die Sinne langsam mir vergehen,
Trägt mich ein Hauch zu morgenroten Höhen.

THEODOR KÖRNER

Who once has looked on beauty with his eyes
Is from that hour given unto death.
All that earth offers turns for him to lies,
And yet he fears to lose his living breath
Who once has looked on beauty with his eyes.

His love of beauty burns, a mortal fire,
Deep in his heart; in vain he hopes to quit
Or satisfy on earth such wild desire,
Who by the dart of beauty once is hit,
His love of beauty burns, a mortal fire.

Like streamlets in hot sand he would surcease,
He yearns to suck in death from winds and skies,
From every blossom he would poison breathe
Who once has looked on beauty with his eyes,
Like streamlets in hot sand he would surcease.

August Graf von Platen-Hallermünde (1796-1835), a master of form who fled from harsh reality into the realm of ideal beauty.

Love of beauty engenders the desire of death — that is the Tristan theme which echoes through much of German thought and literature.

Wer die Schönheit angeschaut mit Augen
Ist dem Tode schon anheimgegeben,
Wird für keinen Dienst auf Erden taugen,
Und doch wird er vor dem Tode beben,
Wer die Schönheit angeschaut mit Augen.

Ewig währt·für ihn der Schmerz der Liebe,
Denn ein Tor nur kann auf Erden hoffen
Zu genügen einem solchen Triebe:
Wen der Pfeil des Schönen je getroffen,
Ewig währt für ihn der Schmerz der Liebe.

Ach, er möchte wie ein Quell versiechen,
Jedem Hauch der Luft ein Gift entsaugen
Und den Tod aus jeder Blume riechen:
Wer die Schönheit angeschaut mit Augen,
Ach, er möchte wie ein Quell versiechen.

AUGUST VON PLATEN

Children on the Bank

"Oh look! You see those water lilies swim
Like clouds, far from the water's rim?
That's pretty! If I had a stick . . . !
As white as snow, with stains like brick,
And combed and curled, primped and fine,
Just like those angels in our shrine.
What do you say? Should I cut off a sprout
From hazelbushes, and try to wade out?
Pooh! — Frogs and pikes can't harm me with their tricks.
Well — I just wonder if the Water Sprite
Squats in those reeds there by the waterside.

I'll go. Well, I am going — I think better not —
I think I saw a face stir in the waves —
Anyway, let's go home. The sun's so hot."

Annette von Droste-Hülshoff, 1797-1848. Her realistic lyricism strove for a harmonious life anchored in religion.

This scene is taken from her cycle, THE POND, which reveals her empathy with all created things.

"O sieh doch! Siehst du nicht die Blumenwolke
Da drüben in dem tiefsten Weiherkolke?
O, das ist schön! hätt ich nur einen Stecken,
Schmalzweiße Kelch' mit dunkelroten Flecken,
Und jede Glocke ist frisiert so fein,
Wie unser wächsern Engelchen im Schrein.
Was meinst du, schneid' ich einen Haselstab
Und wat' ein wenig in die Furt hinab?
Pah! Frösch' und Hechte können mich nicht schrecken —
Allein, ob nicht vielleicht der Wassermann
Dort in den langen Kräutern hocken kann?

Ich geh', ich gehe schon — ich gehe nicht —
Mich dünkt, ich sah im Grunde ein Gesicht —
Komm, laß uns lieber heim, die Sonne sticht!"

ANNETTE VON DROSTE-HÜLSHOFF

My Dear, We Two Were Children

My dear, we two were children,
Playmates in childhood's May;
We scrambled into the henroost
And covered ourselves with hay.

We crowed like cocks, and often
When people would come in view
We suddenly sounded to scare them
Our cock-a-doodle-doo.

Old boxes in our barnyard
We papered and furnished with chairs;
We lived in our stately parlor
And gave ourselves great airs.

Our neighbor's dear old tabby
Came often to bask in our wealth;
We made her fine bowings and scrapings
And asked her about her health

And also the health of her cousins,
And showed her our latest hat;
Since then we have told that story
To many another old cat.

We often sat talking in earnest
And reasoned as old folks may,
How all things were better and finer
And cost so much less in our day;

Mein Kind, wir waren Kinder,
Zwei Kinder, klein und froh;
Wir krochen ins Hühnerhäuschen,
Versteckten uns unter das Stroh.

Wir krähten wie die Hähne,
Und kamen Leute vorbei —
"Kikereküh!" sie glaubten,
Es wäre Hahnengeschrei.

Die Kisten auf unserem Hofe
Die tapezierten wir aus,
Und wohnten drin beisammen,
Und machten ein vornehmes Haus.

Des Nachbars alte Katze
Kam öfters zum Besuch;
Wir machten ihr Bückling und Knickse
Und Komplimente genug.

Wir haben nach ihrem Befinden
Besorglich und freundlich gefragt;
Wir haben seitdem dasselbe
Mancher alten Katze gesagt.

Wir saßen auch oft und sprachen
Vernünftig, wie alte Leut,
Und klagten, wie alles besser
Gewesen zu unserer Zeit;

How faith and love and friendship
Had vanished completely from sight,
And how so very expensive
Was coffee, and money, how tight.

Long gone are the pranks of our childhood,
As faith and friendship are gone;
So money, and world, and the ages
And all things are rolling on.

Translated by JOHN ROTHENSTEINER

Heinrich Heine (1797-1856) was an accomplished romanticist and prophet of socialism.

Heine often combined deep sentiment with elegant ironical mockery.

Wie Lieb und Treu und Glauben
Verschwunden aus der Welt,
Und wie so teuer der Kaffee
Und wie so rar das Geld! —

Vorbei sind die Kinderspiele
Und alles rollt vorbei, —
Das Geld und die Welt und die Zeiten,
Und Glauben und Lieb und Treu.

HEINRICH HEINE

Early when cocks do crow
Ere the stars dwindle,
Down to the hearth I go,
Fire must I kindle.

Fair leap the flames on high,
Sparks whirl drunken;
I watch them listlessly
In sorrow sunken.

Sudden it comes to me,
Youth so fair seeming,
That all the night of thee
I have been dreaming.

Tears then on tears do run
For my false lover:
Thus has the day begun —
Would it were over.

Translated by Charles W. Stork

Eduard Mörike (1804-75) suffered, as did his kindred spirit, Mozart, from tragic premonitions of death amidst the joy of artistic creation.

The Forsaken Maiden illustrates his sympathetic contemplation of reality into which sadness inevitably creeps.

Früh, wann die Hähne krähn,
Eh' die Sternlein verschwinden,
Muß ich am Herde stehn,
Muß Feuer zünden.

Schön ist der Flammen Schein,
Es springen die Funken;
Ich schaue so drein,
In Leid versunken.

Plötzlich, da kommt es mir,
Treuloser Knabe,
Daß ich die Nacht von dir
Geträumet habe.

Träne auf Träne dann
Stürzet hernieder;
So kommt der Tag heran —
O ging' er wieder!

EDUARD MÖRIKE

The Town

The strand is gray, and gray the sea,
And desolate the town;
The mists weigh on it heavily,
And through the stillness moans the sea
Around the lonely town.

No forests high, no birdsong nigh
In air and on the land;
The wild goose lone with clanging cry
Beneath the harvest-moon sails by,
And grass waves on the strand.

And yet, my heart's wrapped up in thee,
Gray town beside the sea.
My youth's enchantment dreamily
Rests evermore on thee, on thee,
Gray town beside the sea.

Translated by JOHN ROTHENSTEINER

Theodor Storm (1817-88) showed in his work the steadfastness of the emerging modern man who has nothing to lean on in his struggle with life except a melancholy remembrance of a better age.

THE TOWN is Husum in northern Germany, and the poem vividly portrays the landscape of Storm's childhood, his own character, and the character of his writings.

Am grauen Strand, am grauen Meer
Und seitab liegt die Stadt;
Der Nebel drückt die Dächer schwer,
Und durch die Stille braust das Meer
Eintönig um die Stadt.

Es rauscht kein Wald, es schlägt im Mai
Kein Vogel ohn Unterlaß;
Die Wandergans mit hartem Schrei
Nur fliegt in Herbstesnacht vorbei,
Am Strande weht das Gras.

Doch hängt mein ganzes Herz an dir,
Du graue Stadt am Meer;
Der Jugend Zauber für und für
Ruht lächelnd doch auf dir, auf dir,
Du graue Stadt am Meer.

THEODOR STORM

Sir Ribbeck of Ribbeck in Havelland

Sir Ribbeck of Ribbeck in Havelland
Had a large pear tree on his land,
And in the golden autumn-tide
When the yellow pears shone far and wide,
When noon struck from the village clock
He filled his pockets with luscious stock,
And if a boy in clogs came running his way
He called, "My boy, have a pear today?"
To a girl he called, "Little maiden fair,
Come on over, I'll give you a pear."

He did this for years, never changing his ways
Until he came to the end of his days.
He knew he was dying. It was autumn-tide
And the pears were shining far and wide.
Then spoke Sir Ribbeck, "Farewell to all!
When I die, put a pear under my pall."
And within three days from the church's nave
They carried Sir Ribbeck to his grave.
And all his tenants and cotters with solemn face
Sang, "Lord Jesus, into Thy grace . . ."
And the children cried from their heavy hearts,
"Who'll give us pears when he departs?"

So cried the children. How little they knew
What even in death Sir Ribbeck could do.
Under the new master the pear and the yard
Are kept under stern and miserly guard.
Sir Ribbeck, however, knowing full well
That his son for a penny his soul would sell,
He knew what he did when he asked his friends
To put in the grave a pear in his hands.
Some three years passed. From the house of the dead
A small pear sapling raised its head.

Herr von Ribbeck auf Ribbeck im Havelland,
Ein Birnbaum in seinem Garten stand,
Und kam die goldene Herbsteszeit,
Und die Birnen leuchteten weit und breit,
Da stopfte, wenn's Mittag vom Turme scholl,
Der von Ribbeck sich beide Taschen voll,
Und kam in Pantinen ein Junge daher,
So rief er: "Junge, wiste 'ne Beer?"
Und kam ein Mädel, so rief er: "Lütt Dirn,
Kumm man röwer, ick hebb' 'ne Birn."

So ging es viel Jahre, bis lobesam
Der von Ribbeck auf Ribbeck zu sterben kam.
Er fühlte sein Ende. War Herbsteszeit,
Wieder lachten die Birnen weit und breit,
Da sagte von Ribbeck: "Ich scheide nun ab,
Legt mir eine Birne mit ins Grab!"
Und drei Tage drauf, aus dem Doppeldachhaus
Trugen von Ribbeck sie hinaus,
Alle Bauern und Büdner mit Feiergesicht
Sangen: "Jesus, meine Zuversicht,"
Und die Kinder klagten, das Herze schwer:
"He is dod nu. Wer giwt uns nu 'ne Beer?"

So klagten die Kinder. Das war nicht recht,
Ach, sie kannten den alten Ribbeck schlecht.
Der neue freilich, der knausert und spart,
Hält Park und Birnbaum strenge verwahrt,
Aber der alte, vorahnend schon
Und voll Mißtrauen gegen den eigenen Sohn,
Der wußte genau, was damals er tat,
Als um eine Birn' ins Grab er bat.
Und im dritten Jahr, aus dem stillen Haus,
Ein Birnbaumsprößling sproßt heraus.

And the years go by like wave after wave
And a pear tree grows above the grave,
And in the golden autumn-tide
Again its pears shine far and wide.
When a boy in clogs comes running its way
Its branches whisper, "Have a pear today?"
To a girl they whisper, "Little maiden fair,
Come on over, I'll give you a pear."

Even today joy spreads from the hand
Of Sir Ribbeck of Ribbeck in Havelland.

Theodor Fontane (1819-98) mirrored in his work the decay of the German petty nobility and middle class.

Sir Ribbeck is an example of Fontane's favorite technique of depicting a whole character through one psychological trait.

Und die Jahre gehen wohl auf und ab,
Längst wölbt sich ein Birnbaum über dem Grab,
Und in der goldenen Herbsteszeit
Leuchtet's wieder weit und breit.
Und kommt ein Jung' über den Kirchhof her,
So flüstert's im Baume: "Wiste 'ne Beer?"
Und kommt ein Mädel, so flüstert's: "Lütt Dirn,
Kumm man röwer, ick geb' di 'ne Birn."

So spendet Segen noch immer die Hand
Des von Ribbeck auf Ribbeck im Havelland.

THEODOR FONTANE

Children

The wine was good that year; and debonair
The tattered beggar staggered from the gate
With florid face, and from his pate
Wavered and flew a shock of silver hair.

And all around him children leapt and ran
And shouted like young Bacchus' votaries;
He tower'd above them, his face full of bliss.
And hundreds of pure eyes mirrored the man.

Next morning peacefully the little dears
Walked in their dreams along the fairy path
While forests were shedding silver tears:

A sudden frost came overnight; its breath
Made the man shudder. Then the cold grew fierce;
He huddled in the bushes, and slept into death.

Gottfried Keller (1819-90) was a foremost representative of poetic realism.

Take life as it is and fill every day with honest effort; death is the end of life, not the beginning of an afterlife — that is Keller's simple message.

Man merkte, daß der Wein geraten war:
Der alte Bettler wankte aus dem Tor,
Die Wangen glühend, wie ein Rosenflor,
Mutwillig flatterte sein Silberhaar!

Und vor und hinter ihm die Kinderschar
Umdrängt' ihn, wie ein Klein-Bacchantenchor,
Draus ragte schwank der Selige empor,
Sich spiegelnd in den hundert Äuglein klar.

Am Morgen, als die Kinderlein noch schliefen,
Von jungen Träumen drollig angelacht,
Sah man den braunen Wald vor Silber triefen.

Es war ein Reif gefallen über Nacht.
Der Alte lag erfroren in dem tiefen
Gebüsch, vom Rausch im Himmel aufgewacht.

GOTTFRIED KELLER

Under the Stars

Who wars in midday heat, and rash and coarse
With fiery hand lashes his team of horse,
Who runs with passion for a goal yet far
Through clouds of dust — he cannot see a star.

But gloomy grow the roads, the horses do not dash.
Dust settles, in the sky the stars begin to flash.
Their everlasting light illuminates God's way.
The battle's still. Night comes to judge the Day.

Conrad Ferdinand Meyer (1825-98) reflected in his poetry the incipient loneliness of the modern man.

Meyer influenced the German poetic style with his lapidary representation of ideas in clear-cut images.

Wer in der Sonne kämpft, ein Sohn der Erde,
Und feurig geißelt das Gespann der Pferde,
Wer brünstig ringt nach eines Zieles Ferne,
Von Staub umwölkt — wie glaubte der die Sterne?

Doch das Gespann erlahmt, die Pfade dunkeln,
Die ew'gen Lichter fangen an zu funkeln,
Die heiligen Gesetze werden sichtbar.
Das Kampfgeschrei verstummt. Der Tag ist richtbar.

CONRAD FERDINAND MEYER

Old Assyrian

In The Black Whale at Ascalon
A man drank night and day
Until as stiff as the stick of a broom
Upon the bar he lay.

In The Black Whale at Ascalon
The landlord said, "I say,
He's drinking of my date palm wine
Much more than he can pay."

In The Black Whale at Ascalon
The waiters at his behest
Hauled in the bill in arrowhead script
On six bricks to the guest.

In The Black Whale at Ascalon
The guest replied: "Oh yeah?
I spent my money long ago
In The Lamb at Nineveh."

In The Black Whale at Ascalon
The clock struck half past four
When the Nubian bouncer pitched
The stranger from the door.

Im schwarzen Walfisch zu Askalon,
Da trank ein Mann drei Tag',
Bis daß er steif wie ein Besenstiel
Am Marmortische lag.

Im schwarzen Walfisch zu Askalon,
Da sprach der Wirt: "Halt' an!
Der trinkt von meinem Dattelsaft
Mehr als er zahlen kann."

Im schwarzen Walfisch zu Askalon,
Da bracht' der Kellner Schar
In Keilschrift auf sechs Ziegelstein'
Dem Gast die Rechnung dar.

Im schwarzen Walfisch zu Askalon,
Da sprach der Gast: "O weh!
Mein bares Geld ging alles drauf
Im Lamm zu Ninive!"

Im schwarzen Walfisch zu Askalon,
Da schlug die Uhr halb vier,
Da warf der Hausknecht aus Nubierland
Den Fremden vor die Tür.

In The Black Whale at Ascalon
No prophet has renown,
And he who would there live in peace
Must lay his money down.

Joseph Victor von Scheffel (1826-86) wrote many songs which acquired lasting popularity with German students.

This irreverent interpretation of the biblical story of the prophet Jonah is typical of the German fraternity songs which turn both biblical and secular history topsy-turvy.

Im schwarzen Walfisch zu Askalon,
Wird kein Prophet geehrt,
Und wer vergnügt dort leben will,
Zahlt bar, was er verzehrt.

JOSEPH VICTOR VON SCHEFFEL

Peace in Arms

Master Fox upon a hill
Once ran into Master Quill.
"What a sight!" spoke Master Fox,
"Are King's orders just for mocks?
Peace has been signed at the court,
Now it's crime and sin to sport
Anything that wounds or kills.
Surrender to me your quills
From the first one to the last."
Spoke the Hedgehog: "Not so fast.
First have all your teeth pulled out,
Then talk peace, and I won't doubt."
And he made himself a ball
Of sharp spines, defying all.
Gentlemen, don't take amiss
A well-armed man, a man of peace!

Wilhelm Busch (1832-1908), an accomplished painter, cartoonist, and satirical poet, lives in American folklore as the originator of the Katzenjammer Kids.

Busch attacked in his verse, as well as in his cartoons, the self-righteousness of the German middle class.

Ganz unverhofft an einem Hügel
Sind sich begegnet Fuchs und Igel.
"Halt!" rief der Fuchs, "du Bösewicht,
Kennst du des Königs Ordre nicht?
Ist nicht der Friede längst verkündigt,
Und weißt du nicht, daß jeder sündigt,
Der immer noch gerüstet geht?
Im Namen Seiner Majestät —
Geh her und übergib dein Fell!"
Der Igel sprach: "Nur nicht so schnell!
Laß dir erst deine Zähne brechen,
Dann wollen wir uns weiter sprechen."
Und alsogleich macht er sich rund,
Schließt seinen dichten Stachelbund,
Und trotzt getrost der ganzen Welt,
Bewaffnet, doch als Friedensheld.

WILHELM BUSCH

Who Knows Where

(Battle of Kolin, 18th of June, 1757)

On bloodied bodies, rubble, smoke,
On grain stalks which the horse-hoof broke
The sunshine lay.
The fight was done. The night sank low.
Many a lad would never go
Home from the fray.

A country squire, young and gay,
Smelled his first powder here today
And had to die.
Although he swung his banner bold
Death took him in her barren hold —
He had to die.

Beside him lay a prayer book.
Where he went, the squire took
With him the tome.
An infantryman from his land
Picked up the prayers soiled with sand
And took them home.

To squire's father brought he fast
This mournful greeting, and the last,
So cold and bare.
The old man wrote with trembling hand:
"Kolin. My son laid in the sand
Who knows where?"

(Schlacht bei Kolin, 18. Juni 1757)

Auf Blut und Leichen, Schutt und Qualm,
Auf roßzerstampften Sommerhalm
Die Sonne schien.
Es sank die Nacht. Die Schlacht ist aus,
Und mancher kehrte nicht nach Haus
Einst von Kolin.

Ein Junker auch, ein Knabe noch,
Der heut das erste Pulver roch,
Er mußte dahin.
Wie hoch er auch die Fahner schwang,
Der Tod in seinen Arm ihn zwang,
Er mußte dahin.

Ihm nahe lag ein frommes Buch,
Das stets der Junker bei sich trug
Am Degenknauf.
Ein Grenadier von Bevern fand
Den kleinen erdbeschmutzten Band
Und hob ihn auf.

Und brachte heim mit schnellem Fuß
Dem Vater diesen letzten Gruß,
Der klang nicht froh.
Dann schrieb hinein die Zitterhand:
"Kolin. Mein Sohn verscharrt im Sand.
Wer weiß wo."

And he who sang for you this song
And you who read it, walk along
Still fresh and fair.
But all of us, the worst, the best,
Once will be laid in sand to rest
Who knows where?

Detlev von Liliencron (1844-1909) blended in his work natural-
istic and impressionistic elements.

A retired army officer turned poet, Liliencron filled his poems
with the excitement of galloping horses, the fragrance of bivouac
fires, and the pathos of lonely death on the battlefield.

Und der gesungen dieses Lied,
Und der es liest, im Leben zieht
Noch frisch und froh.
Doch einst bin ich, und bist auch du,
Verscharrt im Sand, zur ewigen Ruh,
Wer weiß wo.

DETLEV VON LILIENCRON

84 The Drunken Song

O man, what seem
The words, that from deep Midnight stream?
"I was asleep —
I have awakened from my dream.
The world is deep,
Yea, deeper far than Day could deem.
Deep is your Grief,
But deeper Joy than Grief can be.
'Life, be thou brief!' sighs Grief.
But Joy would have Eternity —
Would have deep, deep Eternity."

Translated by CHARLES W. STORK

Friedrich Nietzsche, 1844-1900. Though better known as a
philosopher, Nietzsche was a poet and stylist of the highest order.

With brilliant savagery Nietzsche attacked Christianity as life-
negating, and preached his own gospel of joy and affirmation of
life in this world.

O Mensch! Gib acht!
Was spricht die tiefe Mitternacht?
"Ich schlief, ich schlief —,
Aus tiefem Traum bin ich erwacht:—
Die Welt ist tief,
Und tiefer als der Tag gedacht.
Tief ist ihr Weh —,
Lust — tiefer noch als Herzeleid:
Weh spricht: Vergeh!
Doch alle Lust will Ewigkeit —,
— Will tiefe, tiefe Ewigkeit!"

FRIEDRICH NIETZSCHE

Reproach

No more your noble spirit,
I hear, on strife is bent,
You tread the golden pathways
Of placid world-content.

From agonies and struggle
Your crystal heart is free
Like a huge wave, which finally
Grew tired of the sea,

Which swelled up from the ocean
Where its sisters break
And now sleeps in the woodlands
Turned to a silent lake.

Though summers come to garland
Its banks with hues and smells,
Though from its depth it echoes
Like tolling of the bells,

Though sleepyheaded alders
Its banks with green have crowned,
No storms stir up its waters,
No pearls deck its ground.

Prinz Emil von Schönaich-Carolath (1852-1908), a poet with an awakening awareness of social problems.

This reproach might have been directed at all of Wilhelmian Germany, successful, self-satisfied, heedless of the imminent disaster.

So hast auch du gelassen
Von Groll und edlem Streit,
Du fandest gold'ne Gassen
Der Weltzufriedenheit.

Mich mahnt dein Herz, das helle,
Nun frei von Kampf und Weh,
An eine Riesenwelle,
Die müde ward der See,

Die sich im Überborden
Einst aus dem Meer gewiegt,
Und jetzt, zum Teich geworden,
Tiefblau im Walde liegt.

Wohl deckt mit grünen Flocken
Mitsommers sie das Rohr,
Wohl tönt's wie dunkle Glocken
Aus ihrem Grund hervor,

Wohl nicken grüne Erlen
Darüber schlummerschwer,
Doch hat sie keine Perlen
Und keine Stürme mehr.

PRINZ EMIL VON SCHÖNAICH-CAROLATH

The Workman

We have a bed and we have a child,
   My wife!
And work we've for two all our own to call,
And rain and the wind and the sunshine mild;
We are lacking now but one thing small
To be as free as the birds so wild:
   Time — that's all!

When on Sundays through the fields we go,
   My child!
And see how the swallows to and fro
Are shooting over the grain-stalks tall,
Oh, we lack not clothes, though our share is small,
To be as fair as the birds so wild:
   Time — that's all.

But time! We're scenting a tempest wild,
   We people!
Eternity our own to call,
Else we've no lack, my wife, my child,
Save all that blooms through us, the small,
To be as bold as the birds so wild:
   Time — that's all!

Translated by MARGARET MUENSTERBERG

Richard Dehmel (1863-1920) struggled for the rebirth of man both as a social being and as an individual.

Dehmel succeeded in translating a frankly political theme into poetry of high quality.

Wir haben ein Bett, wir haben ein Kind,
  Mein Weib!
Wir haben auch Arbeit, und gar zu zweit,
Und haben die Sonne und Regen und Wind,
Und uns fehlt nur eine Kleinigkeit,
Um so frei zu sein, wie die Vögel sind:
  Nur Zeit.

Wenn wir sonntags durch die Felder gehn,
  Mein Kind,
Und über den Ähren weit und breit
Das blaue Schwalbenvolk blitzen sehn;
Oh, dann fehlt uns nicht das bißchen Kleid,
Um so schön zu sein, wie die Vögel sind:
  Nur Zeit.

Nur Zeit! wir wittern Gewitterwind,
  Wir Volk.
Nur eine kleine Ewigkeit;
Uns fehlt ja nichts, mein Weib, mein Kind,
Als all das, was durch uns gedeiht,
Um so kühn zu sein, wie die Vögel sind.
  Nur Zeit!

RICHARD DEHMEL

Who Has Passed By A Flame

Who has passed by a flame
To the flame be a thrall!
Though he roam far and wide:
Where its light still can reach
He will not err from truth.
But when he loses its sight,
His own glitter will cheat him.
Lacking the central law
He scatters himself and wastes.

Stefan George (1868-1933) was firmly convinced that it was his mission to regenerate Germany spiritually.

George believed in a Nietzschean aristocracy of spirit and indignantly repudiated Hitler who read into his poems a glorification of the super-race.

Wer je die flamme umschritt
Bleibe der flamme trabant!
Wie er auch wandert und kreist:
Wo noch ihr schein ihn erreicht
Irrt er zu weit nie vom ziel.
Nur wenn sein blick sie verlor
Eigener schimmer ihn trügt:
Fehlt ihm der mitte gesetz
Treibt er zerstiebend ins all.

STEFAN GEORGE

The Die

Thus spake a die: "I fail
To see what I avail;

Because the sixth part of my soul
Though it might have an only eye —
Never beholds the lofty sky
And always just a murky hole."

Hearing this, on which it lay
The sullen earth had this to say:

"You jackass," spake she, "If you park
Your aft on me, of course I'm dark.
I will shine like a precious stone
If you decamp and leave me alone."

The poor die, wounded terribly,
Did not defend its right to be.

Christian Morgenstern (1871-1914) was a deep, religious think-er who preferred to veil his thought in humorous and often non-sensical verse.

Under a thin surface of whimsy, THE DIE records with many other of Morgenstern's poems the imperfections of man.

Ein Würfel sprach zu sich: "Ich bin
Mir selbst nicht völlig zum Gewinn:

Denn meines Wesens sechste Seite,
Und sei es auch Ein Auge bloß,
Sieht immerdar, statt in die Weite,
Der Erde ewig dunklen Schoß."

Als dies die Erde, drauf er ruhte,
Vernommen, ward ihr schlimm zumute.

"Du Esel," sprach sie, "ich bin dunkel,
Weil dein Gesäß mich just bedeckt!
Ich bin so licht wie ein Karfunkel,
Sobald du dich hinweggefleckt."

Der Würfel, innerlichst beleidigt,
Hat sich nicht weiter drauf verteidigt.

CHRISTIAN MORGENSTERN

Ballad of Outer Life

And children grow up slowly with deep eyes
That know of nothing, they grow up and fail
And die, and all men walk their ways.

And bitter fruits grow sweet, drop to the soil
At night, exhausted, like dead birds,
And lie a few days on the ground, and spoil.

And always blows the wind, and always words
Are heard and spoken as we blether,
And pleasantness and weariness recur.

And roads run through the grass hither and thither,
And there are towns with street lights, ponds, and trees,
And some look threatening, others, deathlike, wither.

For what are these built? And for what are these
Endlessly many? And no two the same?
Why always laughter, weeping, and decease?

What good to us is all this and these games,
When we are great, alone eternally,
And wandering never pursue any aims?

Und Kinder wachsen auf mit tiefen Augen,
Die von nichts wissen, wachsen auf und sterben,
Und alle Menschen gehen ihrer Wege.

Und süße Früchte werden aus den herben
Und fallen nachts wie tote Vögel nieder
Und liegen wenig Tage und verderben.

Und immer weht der Wind, und immer wieder
Vernehmen wir und reden viele Worte
Und spüren Lust und Müdigkeit der Glieder.

Und Straßen laufen durch das Gras, und Orte
Sind da und dort, voll Fackeln, Bäumen, Teichen,
Und drohende, und totenhaft verdorrte ...

Wozu sind diese aufgebaut und gleichen
Einander nie? und sind unzählig viele?
Was wechselt Lachen, Weinen, und Erbleichen?

Was frommt das alles uns und diese Spiele,
Die wir doch groß und ewig einsam sind
Und wandernd nimmer suchen irgend Ziele?

What good is it to have seen so much folly?
And yet he says much that says "evening,"
A word from which meaning and melancholy

Issue like honey out of hollow combs.

Translated by WALTER KAUFMANN

Hugo von Hofmannsthal (1874-1929), poet of the pre-war Austrian society which through over-education and over-refinement was losing its ability to live.

His formally flawless poems are void of philosophical substance except for the melancholy, bewildered question about the meaning of life.

Was frommt's dergleichen viel gesehen haben?
Und dennoch sagt der viel, der "Abend" sagt,
Ein Wort, daraus Tiefsinn und Trauer rinnt

Wie schwerer Honig aus den hohlen Waben.

HUGO VON HOFMANNSTHAL

Autumn

The leaves are falling as from lonely heights,
Shed by some distant gardens dying in the sky;
They fall with hints of wistful discontent.

And into solitude from starlit firmament
The heavy earth falls through the nights.

All of us fall. My writing hand falls hence.
And look around: it is the fate of all.

Yet there is One who holds us, as we fall,
With endless solicitude, in His hands.

Rainer Maria Rilke, 1875-1926. His work is a record of a profound mind striving for perfection.

The act of falling was one of Rilke's favorite symbols for existence.

Die Blätter fallen, fallen wie von weit,
Als welkten in den Himmeln ferne Gärten;
Sie fallen mit verneinender Gebärde.

Und in den Nächten fällt die schwere Erde
Aus allen Sternen in die Einsamkeit.

Wir alle fallen. Diese Hand da fällt.
Und sieh dir andre an: es ist in allen.

Und doch ist einer, welcher dieses Fallen
Unendlich sanft in seinen Händen hält.

RAINER MARIA RILKE

Alone

They stretch across this earth-ball,
Roads without number or name,
But all are alike:
Their goal is the same.

You can ride, you can travel
With a friend of your own;
The final step
You must walk alone.

No wisdom is better
Than this, when known:
That every hard thing
Is done alone.

Translated by HERMAN SALINGER

Hermann Hesse (1877-1962), a great defender of individualism, who won the Nobel Prize for literature in 1946.

Hesse's thought is often intricate and difficult, but his verses are a model of simplicity and directness.

Es führen über die Erde
Straßen und Wege viel,
Aber alle haben
Das selbe Ziel.

Du kannst reiten und fahren
Zu zweien und zu drein,
Den letzten Schritt mußt du
Gehen allein.

Drum ist kein Wissen
Noch Können so gut,
Als daß man alles Schwere
Alleine tut.

HERMANN HESSE

Early Autumn

His hair garlanded with barberry crown
Over the stubblefields friend Autumn saunters on.
From the blue winds white gossamer floats down,
The world is dressed in gold and vermilion.

A breath of Autumn scuds across the lea
And shakes the naked vine, last grapes to reap.
From far away, waves of the Eastern Sea
Sing my last summer roses into sleep.

Into the grass ripe apples gently fall,
A lonely guest swings down — a tardy butterfly.
And peace and stillness settle in my soul,
All struggles pass, like wild birds in the sky.

Agnes Miegel (1879-   ) evokes in her powerful ballads the myth and history of East Prussia.

In her landscapes, she penetrates to the soul of the land and of its seasons with the intuitive eye and ear of a woman.

Die Stirn' bekränzt mit roten Berberitzen
Steht nun der Herbst am Stoppelfeld,
In blauer Luft die weißen Fäden blitzen —
In Gold und Purpur glüht die Welt.

Ich seh' hinaus und hör' den Herbstwind sausen,
Vor meinem Fenster nickt der wilde Wein,
Von fernen Ostseewellen kommt ein Brausen
Und singt die letzten Rosen ein.

Ein reifer roter Apfel fällt zur Erde,
Ein später Falter sich darüber wiegt, —
Ich fühle wie ich still und ruhig werde,
Und dieses Jahres Gram verfliegt.

AGNES MIEGEL

The Beggar

His hat was soft like a sponge. His beard
Oozed down over his gray chest,
His wooden leg was trod broad at the end.
Through the shreds of his clothes shone the stars.

Thorns and slugs he wore in his hair,
His eyes inflamed, his rough
And rent face softly bled,
Metallic flies buzzed all around him.

Past winters gnawed in his bones,
Eternity fermented in his bowels,
His blood was blettingsickly, in his
Soul stood petrified forests of memories.

Who rocked you as a child? Who ever loved you?
Come, old man, sit by me. He opens
Silently the abyss of his asking hands,
As black and empty as death, as endless as sorrow.

Wilhelm Klemm (1881-   ) *chose as his central theme the common brotherhood of man.*

This poem is a good example of expressionist technique in which polished thought gives way to daring images and ecstatic phrases.

Sein Hut war mürber Schwamm. Sein Bart
Sinterte über die graue Brust,
Sein Stelzfuß trat sich am Ende breit,
Durch die Fetzen des Kleides irrten die Sterne.

Dornen und Schnecken trug er im Haar,
Seine Augen entzündeten sich, sein herbes
Zerspaltenes Antlitz blutete still,
Metallen surrten die Fliegen um ihn.

In seinen Knochen nagten die Winter,
Ewigkeit gärte durch sein Gedärm,
Faulig krankte sein Blut, in seiner
Seele versteinten Erinnerungswälder.

Wer hat dich als Kind gewiegt? Wer hat dich geliebt?
Komm, Alter, ich will dich hegen. Der aber öffnet
Stumm seiner Hände bittende Abgründe,
Schwarz und leer wie der Tod, groß wie das Leid.

WILHELM KLEMM

Happy Childhood

Something had nibbled on the lips of a girl
Who lay too long in the rushes.
When they opened her chest, her gullet was full of holes.
Finally, under the diaphragm, in a cozy bower
They found young rats, a nestful.
One little sister was already dead.
The others fed on kidney, liver,
Guzzled the cold blood, and so
They spent a happy childhood there.
And swift and happy was even their death:
They threw them all into the water.
Oh, how the little muzzles squeaked!

Gottfried Benn (1886-1956) gave in his poetry a nihilist view of life, life without purpose and direction.

Benn, a physician, often used his hospital experiences to create shocking and brutal images of the vacuity of life.

Der Mund eines Mädchens, das lange im Schilf gelegen hatte,
Sah so angeknabbert aus.
Als man die Brust aufbrach, war die Speiseröhre so löcherig.
Schließlich in einer Laube unter dem Zwerchfell
Fand man ein Nest von jungen Ratten.
Ein kleines Schwesterchen lag tot.
Die andern lebten von Leber und Niere,
Tranken das kalte Blut und hatten
Hier eine schöne Jugend verlebt.
Und schön und schnell kam auch ihr Tod:
Man warf sie allesamt ins Wasser.
Ach, wie die kleinen Schnauzen quietschten!

GOTTFRIED BENN

The Blind Men

Where the blind men come
The trees sough in fright
And the birds screech and check their flight.

Yet they feel no shame
In their crude coats of hair
They smite the road with giant canes.

Their time is short
They do not speak
And always they sniff deathly bleak
In the air
After warmth and light.

Georg Heym (1887-1912) revolted against the sham harmony of Wilhelmian Germany whose violent end he presaged.

Heym's poems contain many apocalyptic visions like that of the blind men.

Wo die Blinden kommen
Rauschen die Bäume vor Schrecken
Und die Vögel schreien in ihren Verstecken.

Aber sie schämen sich nicht,
In ihren härenen Röcken
Und schlagen den Weg mit riesigen Stöcken.

Sie haben nicht Zeit
Und sie sprechen nicht
Und immer schnuppert ihr Leichengesicht
Im Winde herum
Nach Sonne und Licht.

GEORG HEYM

Grodek

The autumn woods ring in the dusk
With clash of deadly weapons; golden plains
And blue seas, over which the sun
Darkly rolls; embraces the night
Dying warriors, the wild accusation
Of their torn lips.
But slowly gathers in the river land
The reddish mist, indwelled by angry gods,
And the spilled blood, and the coolness of moon.
All roads lead into black decay.
Under the golden bough of night and stars
My sister's shadow ghosts among the trees
To hail the eerie dead, to hail their bleeding wounds.
And softly from the rushes pipe autumnal flutes.
Oh, prouder sorrow! ye altars of brass,
Our spirit's flame is fed by searing pain,
Our grandsons yet unborn.

Georg Trakl (1887-1914), *poet of existential despair which heralded Germany's collapse in World War I.*

The sinister beauty of this poem is woven from the last experiences of the poet's short life: the defeat of the Austrian army at the battlefield of Grodek, the memory of his dead sister, his impending insanity and suicide.

Am Abend tönen die herbstlichen Wälder
Von tödlichen Waffen, die goldnen Ebenen
Und blauen Seen, darüber die Sonne
Düster hinrollt; umfängt die Nacht
Sterbende Krieger, die wilde Klage
Ihrer zerbrochenen Münder.
Doch stille sammelt im Weidengrund
Rotes Gewölk, darin ein zürnender Gott wohnt,
Das vergoßne Blut sich, mondne Kühle;
Alle Straßen münden in schwarze Verwesung.
Unter goldnem Gezweig der Nacht und Sternen
Es schwankt der Schwester Schatten durch den schweigenden
    Hain,
Zu grüßen die Geister der Helden, die blutenden Häupter;
Und leise tönen im Rohr die dunkeln Flöten des Herbstes.
O stolzere Trauer! ihr ehernen Altäre,
Die heiße Flamme des Geistes nährt heute ein gewaltiger
    Schmerz,
Die ungebornen Enkel.

GEORG TRAKL

The Flight of Creatures

There is a great unwillingness
In all creatures.
You understand — creatures do not welcome birth.

Even to God's own hand
The world denied itself, and nature
Against its will was born in stars and earth.

Wrapped in warm quilts the world lay
And, like a tired child, resisted
When God came in and sent it out to play.

And all we make and shape,
All through the fingers of our hands,
Our forming hands, wants to escape.

Franz Werfel (1890-1945), lyricist, dramatist, and novelist, is known to the American public from the films THE SONG OF BERNADETTE *and* THE COLONEL AND I, *both based on his works.*

The flight from the harshness of reality, the unwillingness to exist characterizes certain phases of German expressionism.

Es ist ein großer Widerstand
In allem Werk.
Ihr wißt es ja; kein Werk will werden.

So weigerte der Gotteshand
Sich auch die Welt.
Ungern entstanden Stern und Erden.

Die Schöpfung schlief in warmen Decken
Und wehrte sich, das müde Kind,
Als Gott hereinkam, es zu wecken.

Auch was wir bilden und ersinnen,
Will durch die Finger unsrer Hand,
Der formenden, geschwind entrinnen.

FRANZ WERFEL

The Mask Of Evil

On my wall hangs a Japanese woodcut,
A gilded mask of an evil demon.
With pity I contemplate
The swollen veins on his forehead. They betray
What an effort it costs to be evil.

Bertolt Brecht (1898-1956) combined in his plays high poetic and dramatic qualities with engagement in the political struggles of his times.

Brecht believed that evil was an unnatural state caused only by the faulty economic organization of society.

An meiner Wand hängt ein japanisches Holzwerk,
Maske eines bösen Dämons, bemalt mit Goldlack.
Mitfühlend sehe ich
Die geschwollenen Stirnadern, andeutend
Wie anstrengend es ist, böse zu sein.

BERTOLT BRECHT

The Treadmill

Stick out your rump! For someone wants to kick
And if you do not bend he'll miss his trick.
Just do not wonder what the others do:
You can be sure they do it, too.

And so, bend down! He doesn't kick in jest.
They pay him for it. And he does his best.
Deep! Deeper! Nose down to your knee!
It's for our fatherland, you see.

Look at yourself! Enjoy the blue and black
Kicked artfully around your ribs and back.
The best of men have perished by the rough —
Stick out your rump! Enough is not enough!

*Erich Kästner (1899-   ) escaped from disappointing reality
into the world of children, for whom he wrote several classics.
Kästner did not leave Germany even in her darkest hours; he
was one of the few valiant but ineffective voices which were raised
against Hitler.*

Rumpf vorwärts beugt! Es will dich einer treten!
Und wenn du dich nicht bückst, trifft er den Bauch.
Du sollst nicht fragen: was die andern täten!
Im übrigen: die andern tun es auch.

So bück' dich, Mensch! Er tritt ja nicht zum Spaße!
Er wird dafür bezahlt. Es ist ihm Ernst.
Tief! Tiefer! Auf die Knie mit deiner Nase!
Das Vaterland erwartet, daß du's lernst.

Geh vor den Spiegel! Freu dich an den Farben,
Die man dir kunstvoll in die Rippen schlug!
Die besten waren's die an Tritten starben.
Rumpf vorwärts beugt! Genug ist nicht genug!

ERICH KÄSTNER

The Dump

Where the nettles thickest grow
The world-sorrow is forged.
All hear it, and none. When the winds blow
They rock springs from a mattress disgorged.

A gilded old cup — in a curlicue
Of blossoms, these words, like a wraith,
Still legible: Those ever are true —
Charity, Hope, and Faith.

Who joined together, and who broke apart
Those sherds for bitter woe?
Through their enamel, as through a heart,
The burning nettles grow.

A water-filled helmet, rusty and cleft,
For birds to freshen their feather.
Poor soul, whosever body you left,
Who'll join you in mercy together?

Günter Eich (1907-   ) dedicated much of his work to the depiction of the horror and weariness of his time.

Gloomy as it may be, this picture of the human soul, flung like a broken cup on the garbage dump of the world, is not without an undertone of hope.

Über den Brennesseln beginnt,
Keiner hört sie und jeder,
Die Trauer der Welt, es rührt der Wind
Die Elastik der Matratzenfeder.

Wo sich verwischt die goldene Tassenschrift,
Ein Schnörkel von Blume und Trauben,
Wird mir lesbar, — oh wie es mich trifft:
Liebe, Hoffnung, und Glauben.

Ach, wer fügte zu bitterem Schmerz
So die Scherben zusammen?
Durch die Emaille wie durch ein Herz
Wachsen die Brennesselflammen.

Im verrosteten Helm blieb ein Wasserrest,
Schweifenden Vögeln zum Bade.
Verlorene Seele, wen du auch verläßt,
Wer fügt dich zusammen in Gnade?

GÜNTER EICH

Questions of a Workingman Reading History

Who built Thebes, city of seven gates?
My books are full of royal-sounding names.
Tell me: did kings bring stone blocks from the quarries?
Babylon was destroyed who knows how many times.
Who built it up again? And Lima was built of gold.
Did it have golden roofs for its construction men?
And the bricklayers from the Great Wall of China —
Where did they go when their work was done?
Imperial Rome is full of arches of triumph.
Who constructed them? And over whom did the Caesars triumph?
And fabled Byzantium — Did it have only palaces?
Even in legendary Atlantis, as the waves overran it in the night
The drowning men howled to their slaves for help.

Young Alexander conquered India.
Indeed! And was he alone?
Caesar defeated the Gauls.
Did he not have at least a cook around?
Spanish King Philip wept because his fleet
Was swallowed by the sea. Was he the only one to weep?
Frederick the Great won the War of Seven Years.
Who won it with him?

On every page a victory.
Who cooked the banquet for the generals?
Every ten years a memorable man.
Tell me who paid when all his bills fell due!

So many stories.
So many questions.

Wer baute das siebentorige Theben?
In den Büchern stehen die Namen von Königen.
Haben die Könige die Felsbrocken herbeigeschleppt?
Und das mehrmals zerstörte Babylon,
Wer baute es so viele Male auf? In welchen Häusern
Des goldstrahlenden Lima wohnten die Bauleute?
Wohin gingen an dem Abend, wo die chinesische Mauer fertig war,
Die Maurer? Das große Rom
Ist voll von Triumphbögen. Wer errichtete sie? Über wen
Triumphierten die Cäsaren? Hatte das vielbesungene Byzanz
Nur Paläste für seine Bewohner? Selbst in dem sagenhaften Atlantis
Brüllten in der Nacht, wo das Meer es verschlang
Die Ersaufenden nach ihren Sklaven.

Der junge Alexander eroberte Indien.
Er allein?
Cäsar schlug die Gallier.
Hatte er nicht wenigstens einen Koch bei sich?
Philipp von Spanien weinte, als seine Flotte
Untergegangen war. Weinte sonst niemand?
Friedrich der Zweite siegte im Siebenjährigen Krieg. Wer
Siegte außer ihm?

Jede Seite ein Sieg.
Wer kochte den Siegesschmaus?
Alle zehn Jahre ein großer Mann.
Wer bezahlte die Spesen?

So viele Berichte.
So viele Fragen.

                                        BERTOLT BRECHT

Children's Ditty

Who laughs here? And who smiles?
Who smiles is full of wiles.
Who laughs, he is not pleasing —
He must have some dark reason.

Who cries here? Who has cried
Has something bad to hide.
Who cries here out of season
Has some sinister reason.

Who's mum? Who wants to speak?
Who's silent, is a sneak.
Who speaks, has on the sly
Palmed off a dirty lie.

Who plays here in the sand?
Who plays has burnt his hand.
His grounds are clear to all,
He must go to the wall.

Who dies here? Who has died?
What he has done is snide.
To die without a reason
Is perfidy and treason.

Günther Graß (1927-   ) has won reputation with novels of psychological symbolism.

With great economy of expression and verbal wit, Graß conjures the heavy atmosphere of suspicion and distrust reminiscent of Orwell's 1984.

Wer lacht hier, hat gelacht?
Hier hat sich's ausgelacht.
Wer hier lacht, macht Verdacht,
Daß er aus Gründen lacht.

Wer weint hier, hat geweint?
Hier wird nicht mehr geweint.
Wer hier weint, der auch meint,
Da er aus Gründen weint.

Wer spielt hier, spricht und schweigt?
Wer schweigt, wird angezeigt.
Wer hier spricht, hat verschwiegen
Wo seine Gründe liegen.

Wer spielt hier, spielt im Sand?
Wer spielt, muß an die Wand,
Hat sich beim Spiel die Hand
Gründlich verspielt, verbrannt.

Wer stirbt hier, ist gestorben?
Wer stirbt, ist abgeworben.
Wer hier stirbt, unverdorben,
Ist ohne Grund gestorben.

GÜNTHER GRAß

What a Man Is

What a man is, what he has done
We understand when he is gone.
God's song we hear not from the skies
Until we shudder when it dies.

Hans Carossa (1878-1956), a highly cultured humanist, a Goethean, benevolent observer of life.

Was einer ist, was einer war,
Beim Scheiden wird es offenbar.
Wir hören's nicht, wenn Gottes Weise summt;
Wir schaudern erst, wenn sie verstummt.

HANS CAROSSA

The editor and the publishers are grateful for the cooperation of those individuals and publishers who granted permission to use their copyrighted material. Every effort has been made to trace and to acknowledge properly all copyright owners. If any acknowledgment has been inadvertently omitted, the publishers will be pleased to make the necessary correction in the next printing.

"Mother by the Cradle" and "Lullaby," translated from the German by John W. Thomas, in *German Verse from the 12th to the 20th Century in English Translation*, No. 44 University of North Carolina Studies in the Germanic Languages and Literatures. Reprinted by permission of the University of North Carolina Press, Chapel Hill, North Carolina. © Copyright 1963.

"Voice of the People," "Moonlit Night," "The Song of the Swallow," "My Dear, We Two Were Children," "The Town," translated from the German by John Rothensteiner, in *A German Garden of the Heart*, published by B. Herder Book Co., St. Louis, Missouri.

"The Forsaken Maiden" and "The Drunken Song," translated from the German by Charles W. Stork, in *German Masterpieces in Translation*, and reprinted with the kind permission of the translator.

"Wer je die flamme umschritt" from *Der Stern des Bundes* by Stefan George, reprinted by permission of Helmut Küpper Publishing House (formerly Georg Bondi), Düsseldof and Munich.

"Der Würfel" from *Alle Galgenlieder* by Christian Morgenstern; "Ballade des äußeren Lebens" from *Gedichte*, Insel-Bücherei, by Hugo von Hofmannsthal; "Herbst" from *Sämtliche Werke* by Rainer Maria Rilke; and "Was einer ist" from *Gesammelte Werke* by Hans Carossa. Reprinted by permission of the copyright owner, Insel-Verlag, Frankfurt am Main.

"Ballad of Outer Life" from *Twenty German Poets*, edited and translated by Walter Kaufmann. © Copyright 1962 by Random House, Inc.; reprinted by permission of the Publisher.

"Alone," translated from the German by Herman Salinger, reprinted from *Twentieth Century German Verse* by Herman Salinger, by permission of Princeton University Press. © Copyright 1952 by Princeton University Press.

"Allein" from *Stufen* by Hermann Hesse; "Die Maske des Bösen" and "Fragen eines lesenden Arbeiters" from *Gedichte* by Bertolt Brecht; and "Schuttablage" from *Botschaften des Regens* by Günter Eich. Reprinted by permission of the copyright owner, Suhrkamp Verlag, Frankfurt am Main.

"Frühherbst" from *Gesammelte Werke* by Agnes Miegel, reprinted by permission of the copyright owner, Eugen Diederich Verlag, Düsseldorf-Cologne.

"Schöne Jugend" from *Gesammelte Gedichte* by Gottfried Benn, reprinted by permission of the copyright owner, Limes Verlag-Max Niedermeyer, Wiesbaden.

"Grodek," reprinted from the 12th edition of *Dichtungen* by Georg Trakl, published by Otto Müller Verlag, Salzburg.

"Flucht des Werkes" by Franz Werfel, reprinted from *Gedichte aus 30 Jahren*, copyright 1939 by Bermann Fischer Verlag A.-B., Stockholm.

"Die Tretmühle" by Erich Kästner, reprinted from *Bei Durchsicht meiner Bücher*, by permission of Atrium Verlag A.G., Zürich.

"Kinderlied" by Günther Graß, reprinted from *Gleisdreieck*, by permission of Hermann Luchterhand Verlag G.m.b.H., Neuwied.